For Steve and Lynn, champion tidepoolers – K.M.

For my parents – K.C.

First published in Great Britain 2018 by Dean,
an imprint of Egmont UK Limited,
The Yellow Building, 1 Nicholas Road, London, W11 4AN

www.egmont.co.uk

Consultancy by Stephen Savage

ISBN 978 0 6035 7560 0 • 70158/001
Printed in Malaysia

A CIP catalogue record for this title is available from the British Library.

EGMONT
We bring stories to life

Where the SEA Meets the SHORE

KATE MESSNER
Kali Ciesemier

EGMONT

High tide,
sunrise,
a spout of mist . . .

Humpback whales surface to blow,
then dive down deep.
Mother and calf hunt sardines
in the pink morning light.

We have breakfast on Nana's porch
and wait for the beach to come back.

When the muffins are gone,
we trade pyjamas for bathing suits
and race to the water for an early morning swim.

Cold toes,
ocean foam . . .

Between my feet, a sand crab
burrows and disappears into
the safety of the sand.

Icy waves splash our knees, and then we're in!
Dad holds tight to my sister Mia's hands.

Out in the bay,
an otter wraps her pup in kelp.
He'll bob and rest on the surface
while she dives deep to hunt.

The waves creep back,
and the beach returns as I walk the
sliver of shoreline, looking for shells.

A snowy plover pokes along
beside me, searching the seaweed
for tasty treats.

Mia runs up with a splash.
Then she laughs and
cartwheels down the sand.

Out in the bay, the dolphins do
tricks of their own, jumping
and flipping over the waves.

The tide pulls out, but tiny oceans glimmer in rock pools.
The boulders are perfect for hide and seek.
I crouch low so Mia can't see me.
But others have found this hiding spot!

A shore crab darts to its crevice,
legs and claws tucked in tight.

Anemones pull their tentacles
into bodies disguised with
sand and shells.

And a tiny red octopus squeezes into a crack.
Then abracadabra – colour change!
It disappears against the rocks.

Low tide is castle time!
Bucket by bucket, block by block,
our castle rises from the sand.
Water fills the moat.
But the waves stay away.

While pelicans soar in formation,
a tide pool sculpin catches a wave,
going home to its pool in the rocks.

We spread the picnic blanket and dig in
to lunch. Dad sets down his sandwich . . .

And

SWOOP!

A quick, clever seagull flies off
with a treat in its beak.

Now the waves have settled back
and left more rocks exposed.

I hold tight to my sandwich
and climb carefully over
the barnacles.

I peek in pool after pool . . .
Low tide shows the ocean's secrets.
What's appeared in the rocks?
A picnic with a different menu!

Sea stars feast
on mussels.

Moon snails
slurp up clams.

Out in the sea,
bat rays prowl the sandy bottom,
sucking up wiggly shrimp.

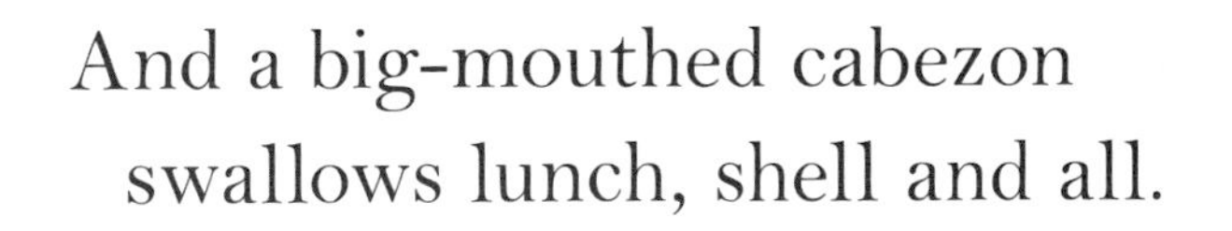

And a big-mouthed cabezon
swallows lunch, shell and all.

"I'm queen of the mountain!" Mia calls.
We climb to the highest rock
and laugh out over the waves.

Just offshore, sea lions call back,
bellowing and barking in play.

A green sea turtle swims past
with slow, quiet flippers and
a face that's old and wise.

The tide comes in and there's just a little beach left. We heap mounds of wet sand to sculpt a turtle of our own. Mia decorates its back with sparkling shells.

Over in the tide pool, a decorator crab makes designs of its own. It covers its shell with algae and sponges to hide.

Soon, a wave whooshes in and
washes our turtle away.

Dad picks up Mia.
But there's time for one last splash.

We stand in the setting sun and watch
dolphins say goodbye to the day.

High tide,
pink sky.

Whales blow . . .
Good night.

DISCOVER MORE

AGGREGATING ANEMONES

Aggregating anemones are often seen as squishy blobs attached to rocks, but when the water is high, you'll recognize them by their flowery antennae waving in the current. These antennae sting and paralyse small animals so the anemones can eat them. Anemones have sticky bumps on their bodies that collect bits of sand and shells. These help them to hide and stop them drying out at low tide.

BARNACLES

Barnacles are creatures that live inside hard, cone-shaped shells on rocks at the beach. At low tide they are hidden, but when the tide comes in they stick out their feathery legs to feed.

BAT RAYS

Bat rays prowl the sandy ocean bottom, flapping their wings to clear away mud and sand to reveal their prey. As they swim along, they suck up food, such as worms, shrimp and clams, like a vacuum cleaner. Shells are no problem for bat rays; they just crunch them with their strong jaws, eat the meat inside and then spit out the shells.

BROWN PELICANS

Brown pelicans fly in formation over the waves looking for fish. They have great eyesight and can spot fish from high in the sky. When they do, they fold back their wings, point their bills at the water and dive. If a pelican catches a fish, it drains the water from its bill and swallows the fish whole, head first.

CABEZON

Cabezon are related to tide pool sculpins. They spend time swimming and feeding in tide pools as well as around kelp forests off shore. They are known to swallow their food whole, eating entire shellfish, such as abalones, and then spitting out the shells.

CALIFORNIA SEA LIONS

California sea lions are often seen – and heard – around rocky beaches. These mammals are known for their noise. Sea lions spend lots of time barking, especially when the males are showing off during mating season. They feed on fish, squid and shellfish. Sea lions have a unique way of keeping warm in the cool waters – by sticking a flipper out of the water to absorb heat from the sun.

DECORATOR CRABS

Decorator crabs use things around them to camouflage themselves. As they're growing, these crabs attach tiny bits of seaweed, anemones and sponges to the back of their shells so they can blend in with their backgrounds to try and avoid being eaten.

GREEN SEA TURTLES

Green sea turtles are reptiles and they can live to be 80 years old. They travel all over the ocean and the females return to the same beaches each year to nest and lay their eggs. Green sea turtles breathe oxygen just like humans. But unlike us, they can spend up to two hours underwater before they need to come up for a breath.

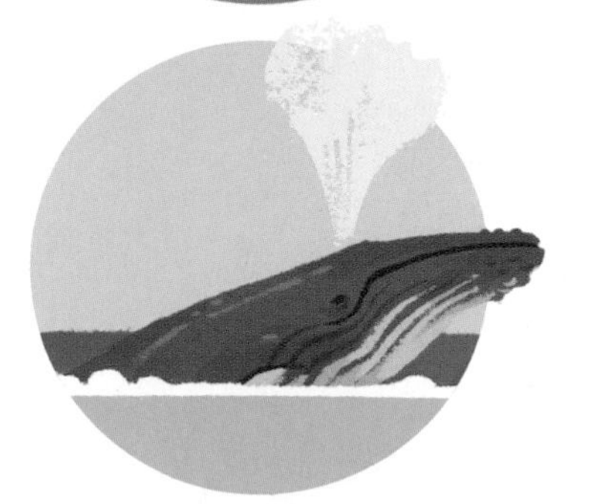

HUMPBACK WHALES

Humpback whales live near coastlines, where they feed on plankton, fish and tiny, shrimp-like crustaceans called krill. They are mammals that must surface sometimes to breathe and expel seawater from their blowholes. They are well known for their songs – moans, cries and grunts – that can travel thousands of kilometres through the ocean.

LINED SHORE CRABS

Lined shore crabs are often spotted skittering around tide pools, but you might not see them for long! They're fast and great at tucking themselves into crevices to hide. These crabs spend about half their time on land and the rest in tide pools. They feed on algae, green seaweeds and small rock pool creatures.

MOON SNAILS

Moon snails move by ploughing through the sand on a muscular foot and have an unusual way of feasting on shellfish. When a moon snail finds a clam, it covers the clam and drills a hole in the shell using its tongue and a special liquid it produces to soften the shell. Then the moon snail sucks out the clam's soft insides.

PACIFIC WHITE-SIDED DOLPHINS

Pacific white-sided dolphins are frequently seen jumping and diving in the waves, hunting for squid and fish. These dolphins often swim in groups of 10 to 100, but some people have spotted thousands in a group.

RED OCTOPUSES

Red octopuses are masters of disguise. Their natural colour is a red or reddish-brown, but they can change colour, turning yellow, brown, white, or even a mix of colours to blend in with their surroundings. They are sometimes seen in rock pools but, as with most animals, it's best to observe but not touch. They have sharp beaks that they use to crack the shells of crabs and other prey.

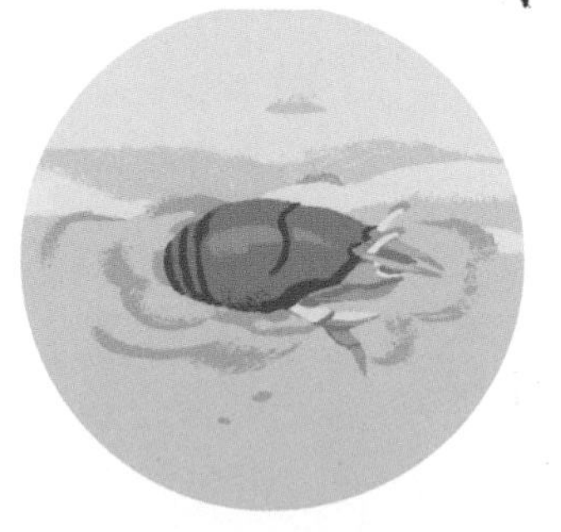

SAND CRABS

Sand crabs spend most of their lives buried in the wet sand where you see waves breaking at the beach. They prepare to feed by burrowing down backwards into the sand and facing the sea with just their eyes and antennae showing. When a wave breaks, the crab sweeps its antennae through the water to filter out tiny plankton to eat.

SEA OTTERS

Sea otters spend much of their time floating on the waves, resting and eating. They often wrap themselves in kelp to keep from drifting. Sea otters eat crabs, sea urchins and shellfish, such as clams and mussels.

SEA STARS

Sea stars, which are often found in rock pools, have an interesting way of eating. They have hundreds of suction cups on their feet, which they use to pry open shellfish. To eat the meat inside, sea stars slide their stomach inside the shell. After they've eaten, they pull their stomach back into their body.

SNOWY PLOVERS

Snowy plovers are sparrow-sized birds that feed along the beach. They eat crabs, worms, insects and shellfish. When you see them feeding, they may look like they're playing in the waves. Plovers often run along the shore, hurrying in and out of the water, stopping every few steps to peck at the sand, looking for food.

TIDE POOL SCULPINS

You may see these big-eyed fish prowling around the bottoms of rock pools. They travel to find food, so when the tide is higher, sculpins will follow the waves from pool to pool, but at low tide, they return to their 'home' pools. They can be difficult to see because they change colour to blend in with their surroundings.

WESTERN GULLS

Western gulls are grey and white birds that seem to love nothing more than stealing snacks at the beach. In nature, gulls eat fish, other marine life and insects. But these birds are also scavengers, which is what makes them picnic pests sometimes.